Rhyming W...
Color, Trace, a...

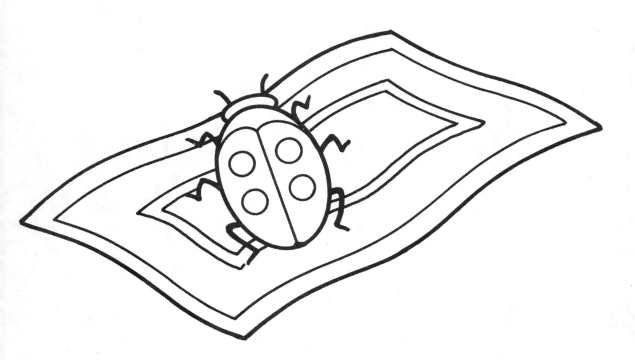

This book belongs to

_____

Cat

cat

Bat

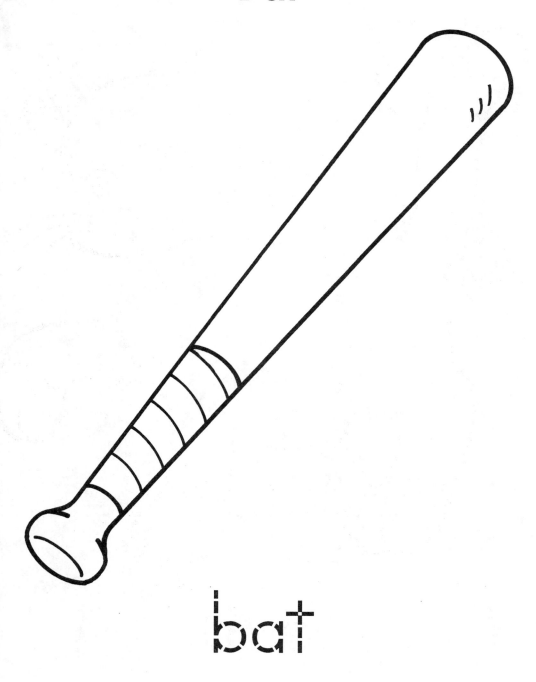

bat

Mop

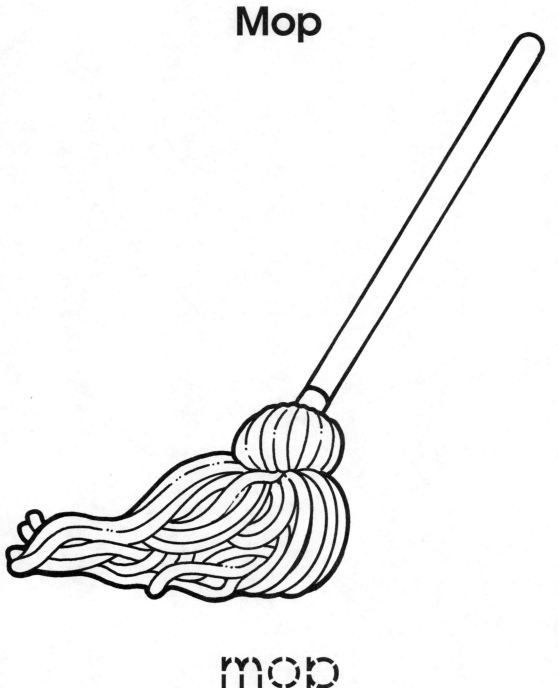

mop

Top

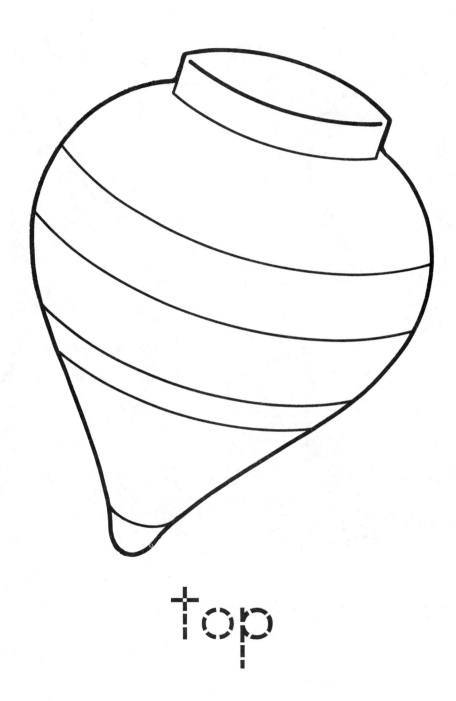

top

Bug

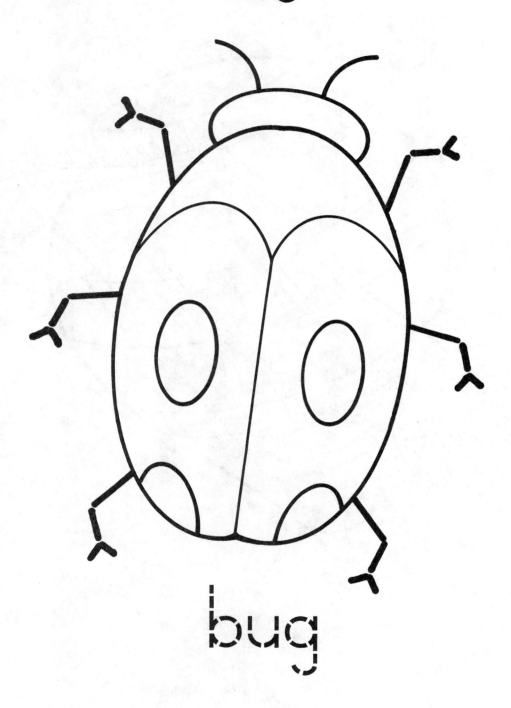

bug

Rug

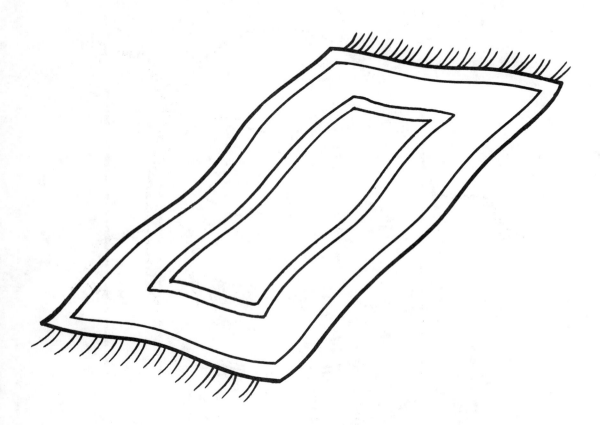

rug

Can

can

Man

man

FS-8186 HH—Rhyming Words: Color, Trace, and Learn

Hat

hat

FS-8186 HH—Rhyming Words: Color, Trace, and Learn

Bat

bat

Mouse

mouse

12

House

house

FS-8186 HH—Rhyming Words: Color, Trace, and Learn

Hen

hen

   FS-8186 HH—Rhyming Words: Color, Trace, and Learn

Ten

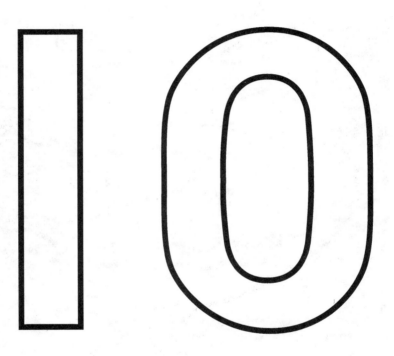

ten

FS-8186 HH—Rhyming Words: Color, Trace, and Learn

Cake

cake

Rake

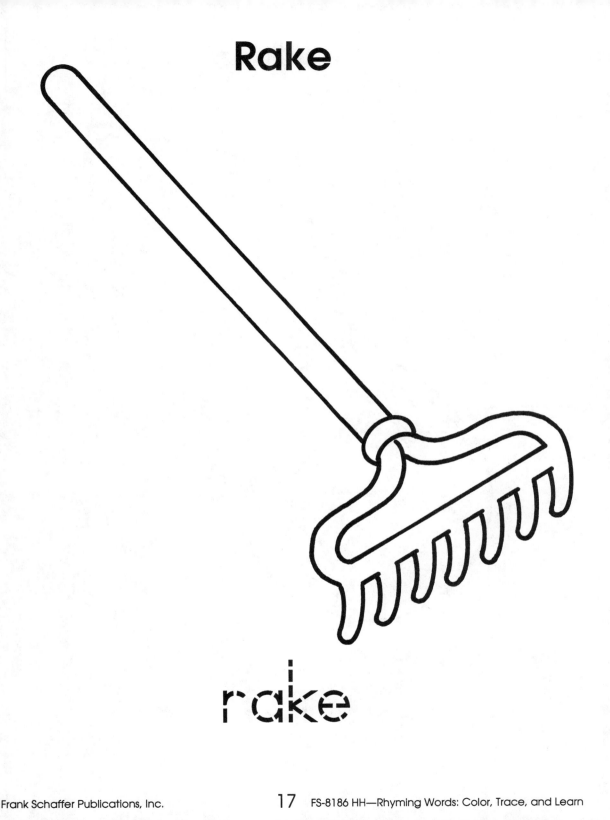

rake

FS-8186 HH—Rhyming Words: Color, Trace, and Learn

Nut

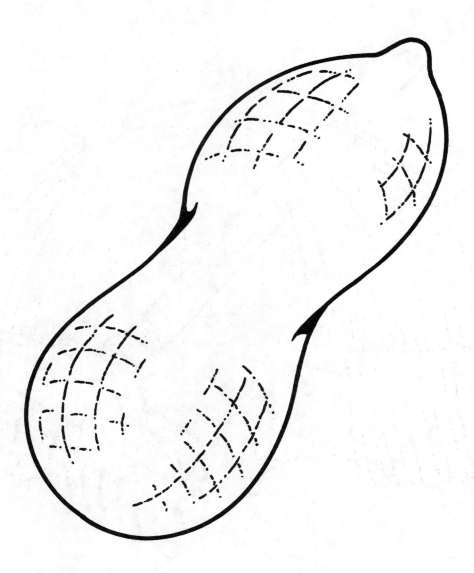

nut

 FS-8186 HH—Rhyming Words: Color, Trace, and Learn

Hut

hut

Pan

pan

20

Fan

fan

21   FS-8186 HH—Rhyming Words: Color, Trace, and Learn

Boat

boat

     FS-8186 HH—Rhyming Words: Color, Trace, and Learn

Coat

coat

FS-8186 HH—Rhyming Words: Color, Trace, and Learn

Fox

fox

Box

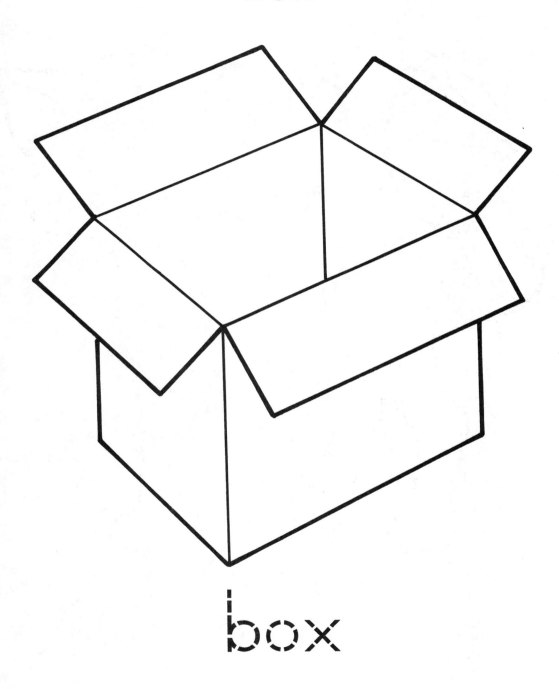

box

 FS-8186 HH—Rhyming Words: Color, Trace, and Learn

Nail

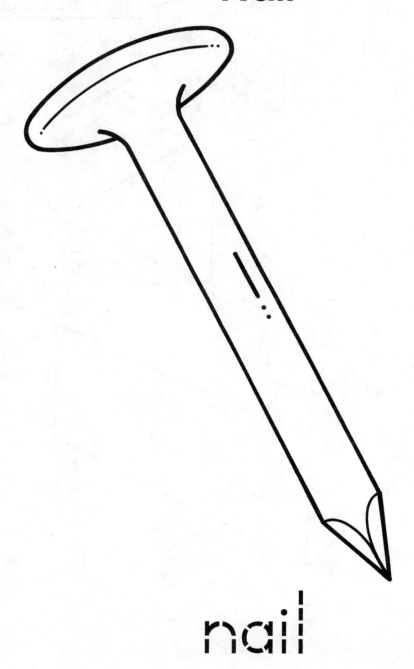

nail

26

Remove these pages from the book. Help your child color and cut out the cards. Have your child match the rhyming words pictured on the cards.

B   FS-8186 HH—Rhyming Words: Color, Trace, and Learn

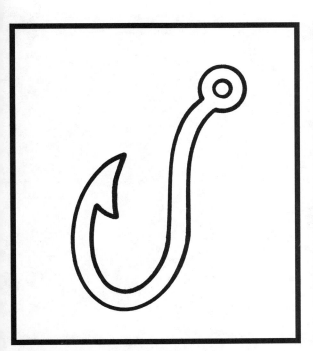

C FS-8186 HH—Rhyming Words: Color, Trace, and Learn

D

Pail

pail

Goat

goat

Boat

boat

29 FS-8186 HH—Rhyming Words: Color, Trace, and Learn

Cup

cup

Pup

pup

31 FS-8186 HH—Rhyming Words: Color, Trace, and Learn

Sock

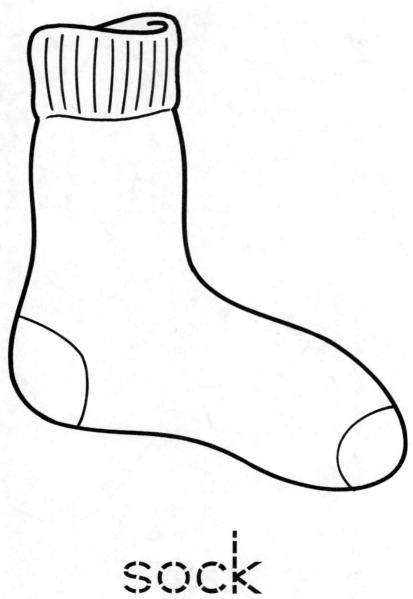

sock

Lock

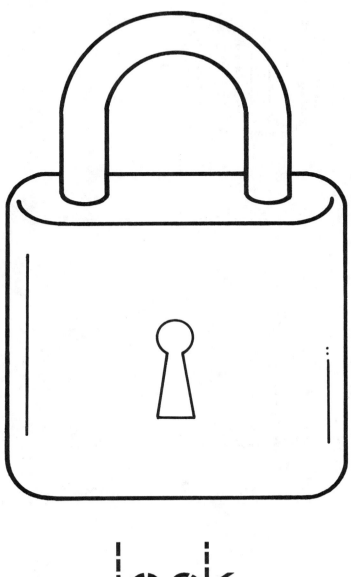

lock

Duck

duck

34

Truck

truck

Cake

cake

Snake

snake

FS-8186 HH—Rhyming Words: Color, Trace, and Learn

Car

car

FS-8186 HH—Rhyming Words: Color, Trace, and Learn

Star

star

39

Bee

bee

FS-8186 HH—Rhyming Words: Color, Trace, and Learn

Tree

Tree

41

Sock

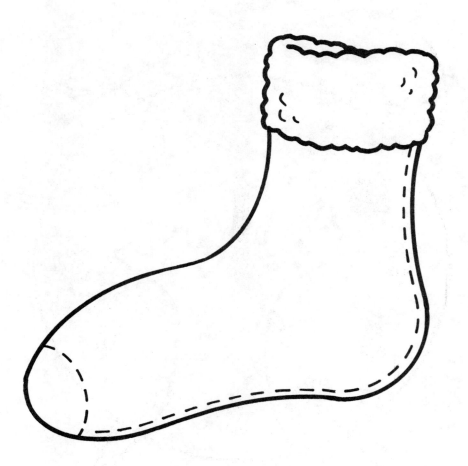

sock

Clock

clock

FS-8186 HH—Rhyming Words: Color, Trace, and Learn

Bag

bag

FS-8186 HH—Rhyming Words: Color, Trace, and Learn

Flag

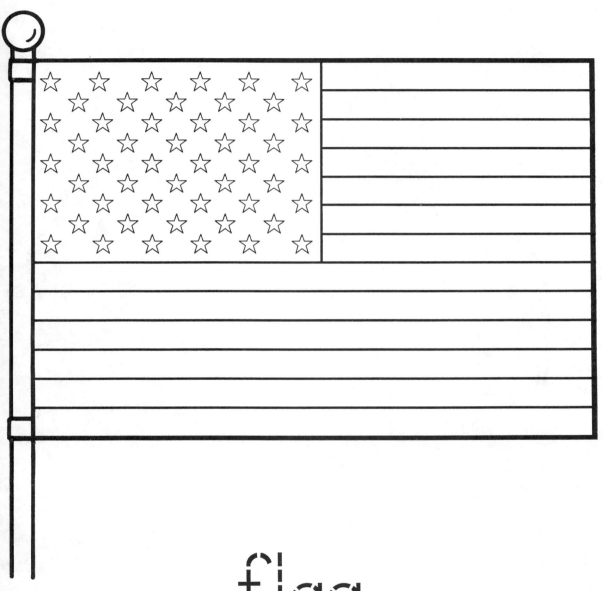

flag

45

Rock

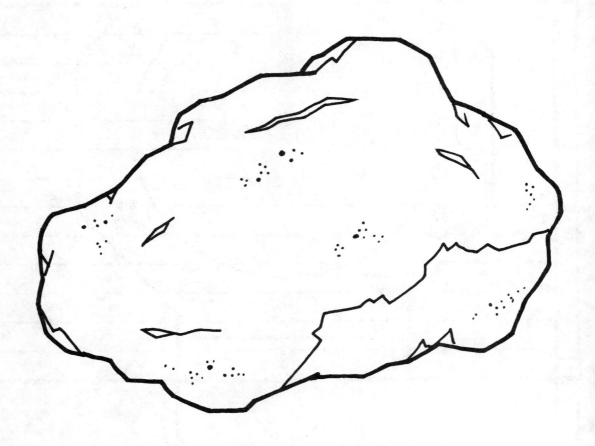

rock

Clock

clock

47

Log

log

 FS-8186 HH—Rhyming Words: Color, Trace, and Learn

Frog

frog

49 FS-8186 HH—Rhyming Words: Color, Trace, and Learn

Bed

bed

 FS-8186 HH—Rhyming Words: Color, Trace, and Learn

Sled

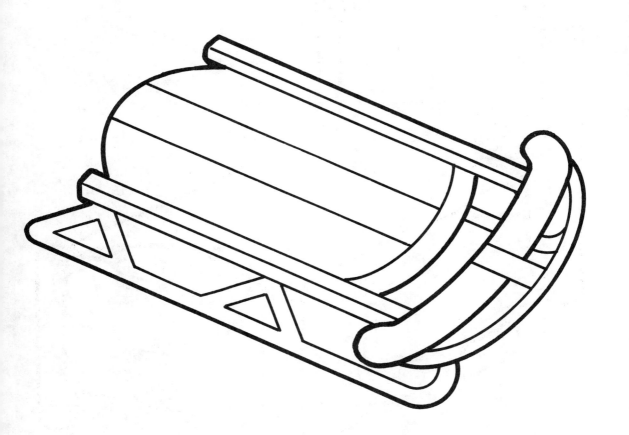

sled

51

Draw lines to match the pictures that rhyme.